HOW FIRE CAME TO EARTH
═CAME TO═
EARTH

Once there was no fire on earth.

Only the Sky People had fire.

In winter the animals were cold.

"Who will go and get fire
from the Sky People?" they said.

"I will," said Rabbit.
"But you will have to help me."

So Rabbit made a big,
feather headdress.
He put it on and set out
for the Sky People's village.
"Hello, Sky People," said Rabbit.
"I have come to teach you
a new dance. Look at my
wonderful dancing hat."

Rabbit began to dance.
Around and around the fire
he danced.
Soon all the Sky People
were dancing, too.
As he danced Rabbit bent
lower and lower until...

Whoosh! The feathers caught fire.

Rabbit began to run.

"Stop! Stop!" shouted the Sky People.

"Give us back our fire!"

And they chased after Rabbit.

Soon Rabbit was tired.

"Squirrel, Squirrel,
take the headdress," panted Rabbit.

So Squirrel took the headdress
and ran.

The fire was so hot the heat
made her tail curl over her back.

And to this day,
squirrels' tails are this way.

Soon Squirrel was tired.

"Crow, Crow, take the headdress," panted Squirrel.

So Crow took the headdress and flew.

The smoke from the fire turned all his feathers black.

And to this day, crows' feathers are this way.

Soon Crow was tired.

"Raccoon, Raccoon,

take the headdress," panted Crow.

So Raccoon took the headdress

and ran.

The hot ash from the fire

burned rings on her tail.

And to this day,

raccoons' tails are this way.

Soon Raccoon was tired.

"Turkey, Turkey, take the headdress,"
panted Raccoon.

So Turkey took the headdress
and ran.

The fire burned all the feathers
off his head.

And to this day,
turkeys' heads are this way.

But Turkey was not a fast runner.

The Sky People

were catching up with him,

and the fire was nearly out.

"Set my tail on fire," said Deer.

So Turkey set Deer's tail on fire.

Deer ran through the woods.
As she ran, she flicked her tail
from side to side.
"Trees, Trees, hide the fire,"
panted Deer.
The trees took the fire
and hid it in their wood.
The fire burned off
most of Deer's tail.
And to this day,
most deer's tails are this way.

The Sky People
went back to their village.
The trees had hidden the fire
and they couldn't find it. But Rabbit
knew how to find it again.
He showed the animals
how to make fire
by rubbing two pieces of wood
together.

So the animals had fire
to keep them warm in winter.
But to this day,
some of them have never
looked the same again.